NEW CHART HITS
Playalong *for* Alto Saxophone

Wise Publications
PART OF THE MUSIC SALES GROUP
London/New York/Paris/Sydney/Copenhagen/Berlin/Madrid/Tokyo

Published by:
Wise Publications
8/9 Frith Street, London W1D 3JB, England.

Exclusive Distributors:
Music Sales Limited
Distribution Centre, Newmarket Road, Bury St. Edmunds,
Suffolk IP33 3YB England.
Music Sales Pty Limited
120 Rothschild Avenue, Rosebery, NSW 2018, Australia.

Order No. AM963072
ISBN 0-7119-8067-5
This book © Copyright 2003 by Wise Publications.

Compiled by Nick Crispin.
Music arranged by Simon Lesley.
Music processed by Enigma Music Production Services.
Cover photography by George Taylor.
Printed in Great Britain.

CD recorded, mixed and mastered by Jonas Persson.
Backing tracks by Danny G.
Instrumental solos by John Whelan.

Your Guarantee of Quality:
As publishers, we strive to produce every book to
the highest commercial standards.
The music has been freshly engraved and the book has been
carefully designed to minimise awkward page turns and
to make playing from it a real pleasure.
Particular care has been given to specifying acid-free, neutral-sized
paper made from pulps which have not been elemental chlorine bleached.
This pulp is from farmed sustainable forests and was
produced with special regard for the environment.
Throughout, the printing and binding have been planned to
ensure a sturdy, attractive publication which should give years of enjoyment.
If your copy fails to meet our high standards,
please inform us and we will gladly replace it.

www.musicsales.com

Saxophone
Fingering Chart

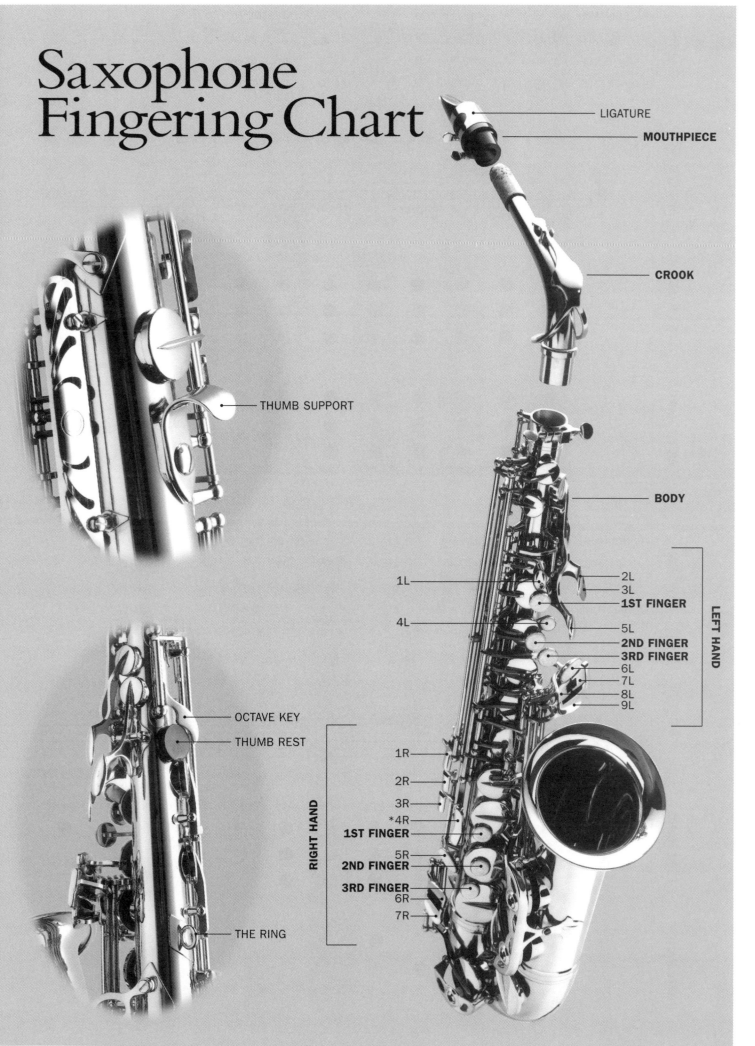

LIGATURE

MOUTHPIECE

CROOK

THUMB SUPPORT

BODY

OCTAVE KEY

THUMB REST

THE RING

1L
2L
3L
1ST FINGER
4L
5L
2ND FINGER
3RD FINGER
6L
7L
8L
9L

LEFT HAND

1R
2R
3R
*4R
1ST FINGER
5R
2ND FINGER
3RD FINGER
6R
7R

RIGHT HAND

* Not fitted on some saxophones

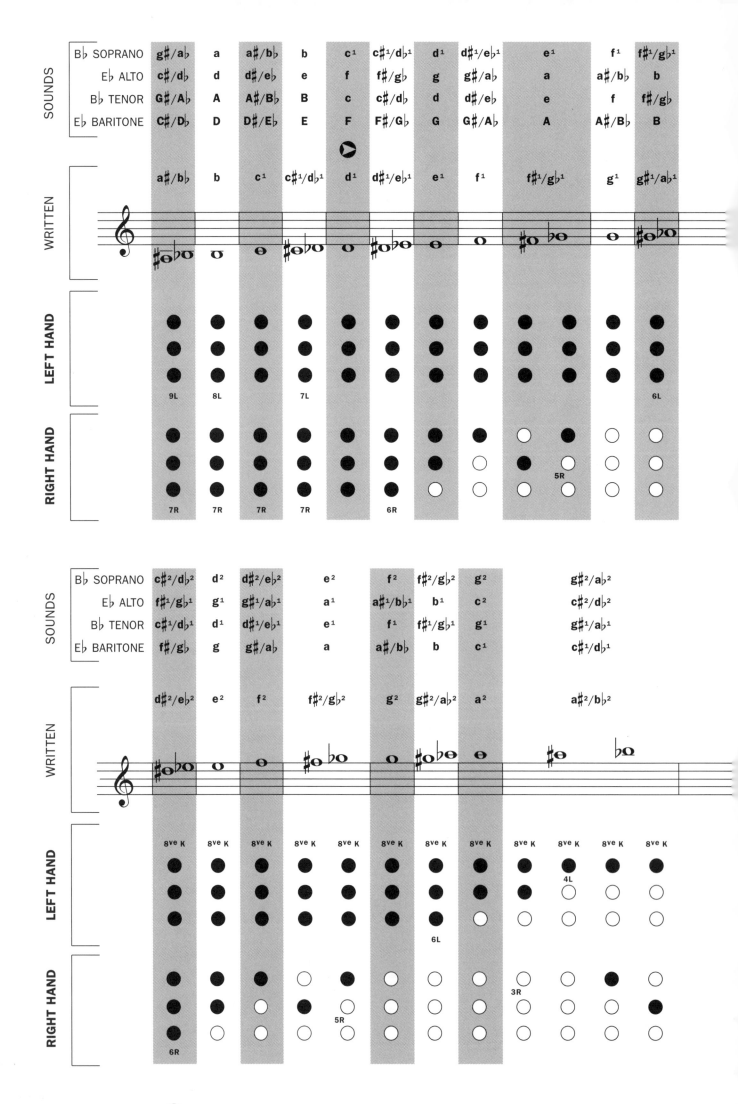

Indicates the lower limit of the best playing range

g¹	g#¹/ab¹	a¹	a#¹/bb¹	b¹	c²
c¹	c#¹/db¹	d¹	d#¹/eb¹	e¹	f¹
g	g#/ab	a	a#/bb	b	c¹
c	c#/db	d	d#/eb	e	f

| a¹ | a#¹/bb¹ | b¹ | c² | c#²/db² | d² |

8ve K   8ve K

4L

7L

3R   2R

7R

a²	a#²/bb²	b²	c³	c#³/db³	d³	d#³/eb³
d²	d#²/eb²	e²	f²	f#²/gb²	g²	g#²/ab²
a¹	a#¹/bb¹	b¹	c²	c#²/db²	d²	d#²/eb²
d¹	d#¹/eb¹	e¹	f¹	f#¹/gb¹	g¹	g#¹/ab¹

| b² | c³ | c#³/db³ | d³ | d#³/eb³ | e³ | f³ |

8ve K   8ve K   8ve K   8ve K   8ve K   8ve K   8ve K   8ve K   8ve K   8ve K

1L   1L

3L   2L   2L   2L
          3L   3L   3L
                                5L

2R   1R   1R

Indicates the upper limit of the best playing range

Anyone Of Us (Stupid Mistake)

Words & Music by Jörgen Elofsson, Per Magnusson & David Kreuger

Colourblind

Words & Music by Darius, Pete Glenister & Denny Lew

Repeat to fade

Complicated

Words & Music by Lauren Christy, David Alspach, Graeme Edwards & Avril Lavigne

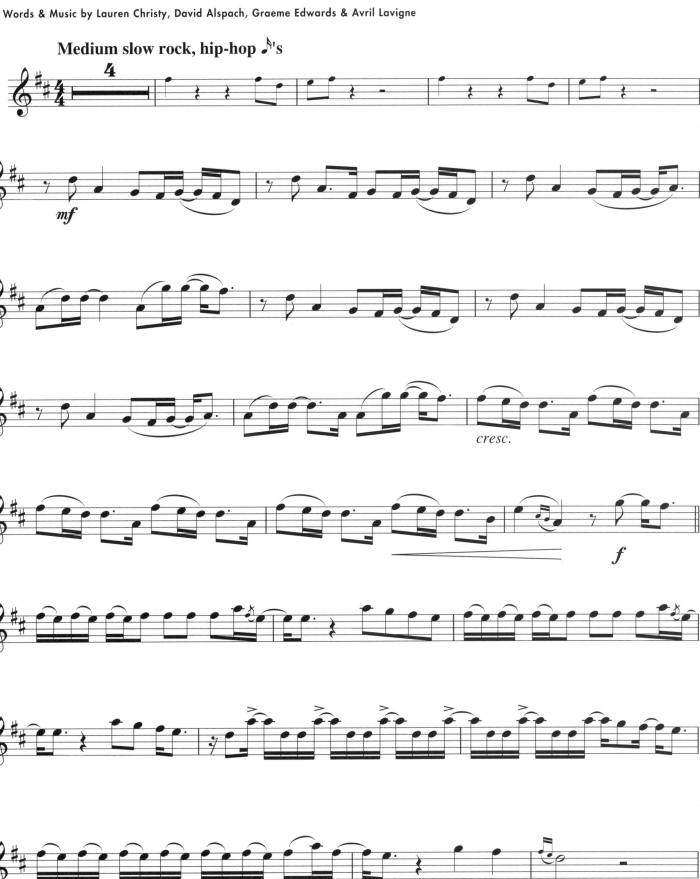

If You're Not The One

Words & Music by Daniel Bedingfield

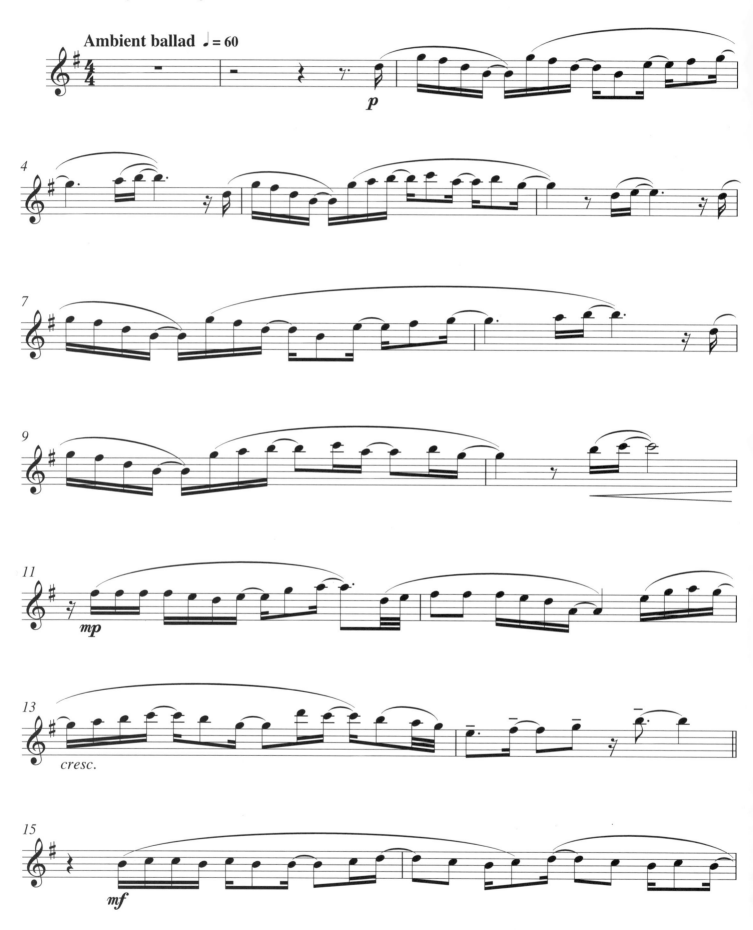

I'm Gonna Getcha Good!

Words & Music by Shania Twain & Robert John "Mutt" Lange

Line-dancing rock ♩ = 124

Love At First Sight

Words & Music by Kylie Minogue, Richard Stannard, Julian Gallagher, Ash Howes & Martin Harrington

Round Round

Words & Music by Brian Higgins, Timothy Powell, Miranda Cooper, Felix Strecher, Robin Hoffman,
Rino Spadavecchia, Florian Pfleuger, Keisha Buchanan, Mutya Buena, Heidi Range, Nicholas Coler & Lisa Cowling

Tempo primo

The Tide Is High (Get The Feeling)

Words & Music by John Holt, Howard Barrett, Tyrone Evans, Bill Padley & Jem Godfrey

Sing-along pop ♩ = 104

Unbreakable

Words & Music by Jorgen Elofsson & John Reid

Whenever, Wherever

Words by Shakira & Gloria Estefan
Music by Shakira & Tim Mitchell